Insect Countdown

by Alex Ives

SCHOLASTIC INC.

New York Toronto London Auckland Sydney New Delhi Hong Kong

Photo Credits

Cover (bg: t) tanatat/Shutterstock, (bg: b) SergeyIT/Shutterstock, (butterfly) Ambient Ideas/Shutterstock, (bee) rodho/Shutterstock, (ladybug left) Yellowj/Shutterstock, (ladybug right) irin-k/Shutterstock, (grasshopper) iStockphoto/Thinkstock; p. 2 (ants) Juraj Kovac/Shutterstock, Kesu/Shutterstock, asharkyu/Shutterstock, Evgeniy Ayupov/Shutterstock, (bg) maxstockphoto/Shutterstock, Dario Sabljak/Shutterstock; p. 3 (ladybugs) irin-k/Shutterstock, Yellowj/Shutterstock, Dionisvera/Shutterstock, (r) Ilya Akinshin/Shutterstock, (bg) Subbotina Anna/Shutterstock; p. 4 (crickets) Luis Carlos Jimenez del rio/Shutterstock, alle/Shutterstock, Attl Tibor/Shutterstock, (music notes) argus/Shutterstock, (fg) jannoon028/Shutterstock, (bg) Krivosheev Vitaly/Shutterstock, yamix/Shutterstock; p. 5 (bees) rodho/Shutterstock, Pan Xunbin/Shutterstock, (beehive) phloen/Shutterstock, (bg) photowings/Shutterstock, vilax/Shutterstock; p. 6 (grasshoppers) dragi52/Shutterstock, iStockphoto/Thinkstock, (bg) Andreas berheide/Shutterstock, SergeyIT/Shutterstock; p. 7 (fg) iStockphoto/Thinkstock, (bg) LiliGraphie/Shutterstock; p. 8 (fg) Le Do/Shutterstock, Jag_cz/Shutterstock, (bg) SergeyIT/Shutterstock.

Designed by Amy Lam.

No part of this publication may be reproduced in whole or in part, or stored in a retrieval system, or transmitted in any form or by any means, electronic, mechanical, photocopying, recording, or otherwise, without written permission of the publisher. For information regarding permission, write to Scholastic Inc., 557 Broadway, New York, NY 10012.

Copyright © 2014 by Scholastic Inc.
All rights reserved. Published by Scholastic Inc.
Printed in the U.S.A.
Produced by Clean Slate Press Ltd.

ISBN-13: 978-0-545-64840-0
ISBN-10: 0-545-64840-8

SCHOLASTIC and associated logos are trademarks
and/or registered trademarks of Scholastic Inc.

10   40   23 22 21 20 19 18

Seven little insects creep
up the hill.

7 ants

Six little insects creep
on a flower.

6 ladybugs

Five little insects sing in the grass.

5 crickets

Four little insects live
in a hive.

4 bees

Three little insects hop
in the grass.

3 grasshoppers

Two little insects chew
on the leaves.

2 caterpillars

And one little insect flies
to the flower!

1 butterfly